MW01009943

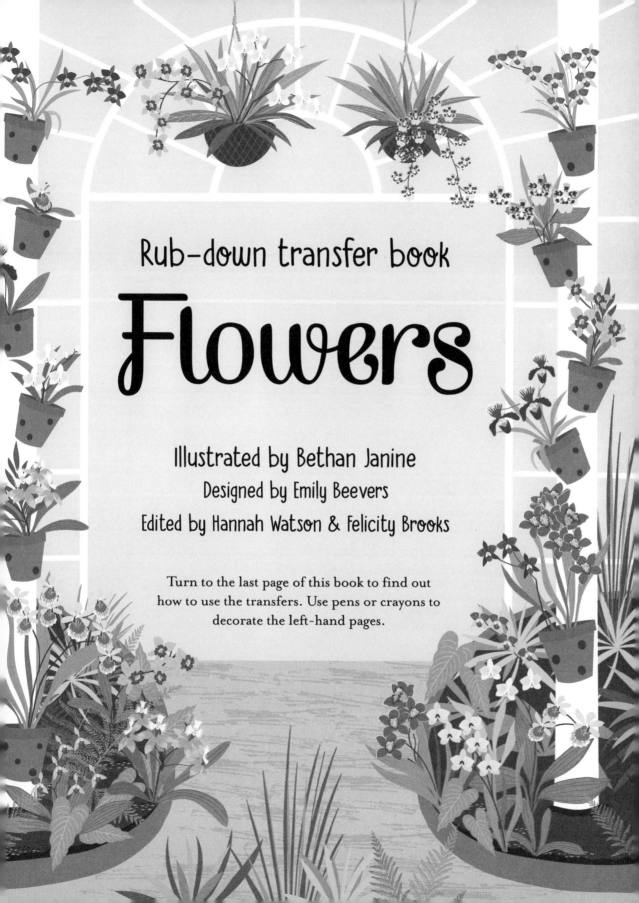

Rub-down transfer book

Flowers

Illustrated by Bethan Janine
Designed by Emily Beevers
Edited by Hannah Watson & Felicity Brooks

Turn to the last page of this book to find out
how to use the transfers. Use pens or crayons to
decorate the left-hand pages.

Summer meadow

Cornflower

Corn poppy

Corncockle

Red clover

By the coast

Rock sea-spurrey

Sea pink

English stonecrop

Spring squill

Small copper

Prairie flowers

Great blue lobelia

Prairie coneflower

Prairie rose

Greenhouse alpines

Thyme

Stemless gentian

Bird's-eye primrose

Alpine toadflax

Sempervivum

Desert in bloom

Bigelow's monkeyflower

Dune sunflower

Lupine flower

Desert sand-verbena

Rose trellis

Savanna flowers

Groundsel

Monarch-of-the-ve

Ice plant

Bokkeveld pride

Orchid house

Cattleya orchid

Slipper orchid

Boat orchid

Dancing-lady orchid

Spring blooms

Hyacinth

Bluebell

Pansy

Daffodil

Sweet peas

Auriculas

How to use this book

To fill the scenes with flowers, you'll need a ballpoint pen or a pencil to add the rub-down transfers to the right-hand pages of this book. You can use crayons or felt-tip pens to decorate the left-hand pages.

Take the transfer sheets out of their pocket at the front of the book and find the one with the symbol that exactly matches the symbol on the pages you want to work on. (Most sheets contain the transfers for two scenes.) Remove the backing sheet.

| To use the transfers, position one of the little pictures over the place you want it to go in the scene. | Scribble all over it firmly with a pencil or ballpoint pen, taking care not to touch any of the pictures around it. | When you have completely covered the transfer, gently lift off the transfer sheet to reveal the new picture. |

First published in 2018 by Usborne Publishing Ltd., Usborne House, 83-85 Saffron Hill, London EC1N 8RT, England. Printed in China.

Copyright ©2018 Usborne Publishing Ltd. The name Usborne and the devices 🌱🎈 are Trade Marks of Usborne Publishing Ltd. All rights reserved. No part of this publication may be reproduced, stored in a retrieval system, or transmitted in any form or by any means, electronic, mechanical, photocopying, recording or otherwise without the prior permission of the publisher. UE.